22922

For Gabriel

First published in 2009 in Great Britain by
Barrington Stoke Ltd
18 Walker Street, Edinburgh, EH3 7LP

www.barringtonstoke.co.uk

Copyright © 2009 Stephen Potts
Illustrations © Nigel Dobbyn

ISBN: 978-1-84299-691-1

Printed in Great Britain by Bell & Bain Ltd

Contents

Chapter 1
Tail Back

Rain drummed down on the car roof above Rob's head. The wind-screen wipers swished from side to side. Between swishes Rob watched the rain bounce off the roofs of the cars in front and beside. All of them were stopped. The motorway had become a giant car park.

His mum turned off the wipers and then the engine. The rain sounded louder now. She sighed, then leaned forward to switch the radio on.

"Let's see if we can get some traffic news," she said. She sat back, turned towards Rob and smiled. "How was it today?"

Rob gave a shrug. "The same as ever. Boring."

"Was Doctor Calvert there?"

"Yes. She said my blood tests were good." He yawned. "But I still feel really tired, whatever they say."

"What about your school-work?"

Rob waved an exercise book at her. "Done most of it. It helped take the boredom away."

Rob fiddled with the button on the door, the one that lowered the window. A police car went by on the side of the road. The traffic coming the other way wasn't going fast – but it was at least moving.

Rob had come to hate this road. For two long years he had used it three times every week, going to and from the hospital for his kidney treatment.

He did some sums in his head. "30,000," he said.

"30,000 what?" asked his mum.

"Since I got ill, we've done 30,000 miles on this road."

"Don't think about it that way, Robbie." She fiddled again with the radio.

"That's enough to go right round the world. Or anywhere we wanted, for a holiday." The need for kidney treatment stopped Rob travelling. And if he couldn't go, nor could his family.

There was a low thrumming noise. Rob looked up. The noise grew louder, until his mum noticed it too. Thinking it was the radio, she switched it off – but the noise didn't stop. Instead it went on getting louder until it seemed to fill the car. When the whole car shook with it Rob knew what the noise was. "A helicopter!"

Rob pushed the button on his door handle. The window slid down, letting the rain in. Big drops fell on his exercise book and made the ink run. He stuck his head out and looked up. A red helicopter, marked with a white cross, flew close over-head. It was moving slowly, and getting lower. An orange light on its tail flashed brightly, in a double pulse. *Like a heart beat*, Rob thought, as if the helicopter was a living thing.

His mum pushed her own button to close his window, and Rob ducked his soaking head back inside just in time.

"Put the wind-screen wipers on!" he pleaded, leaning forward to watch the helicopter as it came closer and closer. Beyond the cars in front he saw a mass of flashing lights – red for a fire engine, blue for police cars and ambulances. And now orange for the helicopter as it neared the ground.

"He's landing on the road!" Rob shouted.

"That's why we've stopped, then. It's the air ambulance. They've closed the road to let it land. There must be a nasty accident ahead."

The helicopter was hidden behind the traffic. Rob could just make out its rotor-blades which slowly stopped spinning as the engine noise died away. Everything was still again, apart from the rain.

Rob and his mum both tried not to think about what might be happening just ahead of them. They tried not to picture the sight of blood and broken bones, or the sound of saws as firemen cut through twisted metal. They tried not to smell the leaking petrol, or feel the scrunch of broken glass on the ground. It wasn't easy.

To take these thoughts away, Mum put the radio on, and set the volume high. Rob listened to the music, and the sports news, and the headlines, but he kept watching the helicopter rotor-blades. Five or six songs went by before they started spinning again; very slowly at first, and then faster and faster. The engine roared into life, even louder than before.

The helicopter rose slowly until Rob could see again the flashing light on its tail and the white cross on its side. When it was clear of the cars and lorries it rose faster, and then sped off, back the way it had come, back towards the hospital where Rob spent every Monday, every Wednesday and every Friday afternoon.

It wasn't long before the traffic jam began to clear. Mum started the engine and drove slowly forward, towards the crash. Two cars and a van had been moved to the side of the road. One of the cars was upside down, and badly smashed.

Rob turned round and looked through the back window as Mum drove on. In the sky above the crash, far away, he could just make out the helicopter's tail light. He thought about the person on the stretcher inside. *Man or woman? Girl or boy? Awake or in a coma? Likely to live ... or not?*

"Hope you make it," he murmured, as the tail light flashed for the last time and vanished from view. "Whoever you are."

Kidneys and the jobs they do

1. Most of us have two kidneys, one on each side. They are safely tucked under your ribs, about half-way down your back.

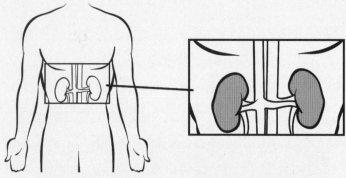

2. Each kidney is about the same size as your fist.

3. We can normally cope with one kidney, if the other one gets damaged by an illness or injury. It's like carrying a spare.

4. If both kidneys get damaged we get ill. It's called **kidney failure**. It can happen at any age. Rob was nine when it happened to him.

5. The kidneys do several jobs. The most important is to clean, or **filter**, the blood, and remove harmful substances, which we then pass out in our pee (which doctors call **urine**).

6. The kidneys also keep the right balance of salt and water in our bodies. They do this by matching the amount we sweat or pee out to the amount we drink. They keep our systems in balance. If they didn't we would get dried out like a raisin, or soggy like a sponge.

Chapter 2
Transplant Time

Captain Robert Murray gripped the controls of his space fighter as it sped towards the invading alien fleet. An alarm rang somewhere deep in the engine room, followed by low urgent voices. He ignored them.

"Fire thought missiles!" he said to his computer. And at once a stream of silver rockets flashed through space. There was a huge flash when the first alien ship was hit and –

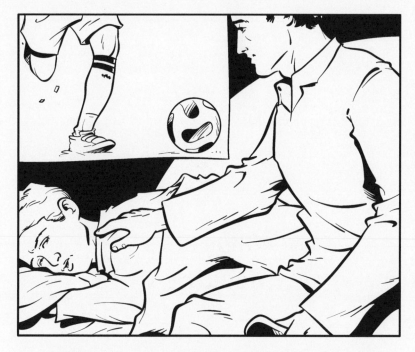

"Wake up, son." Rob's father stood in the bedroom doorway. Light poured in from the hall beyond. He was bleary-eyed, and his pyjamas were crumpled, but he was smiling. He waved the phone in his hand.

"That was the hospital calling."

Rob was still half in his dream. His father might have been speaking Klingon for all the sense he made.

"Huh?" he mumbled. "What?"

His father sat on Rob's bed and smiled again. "They've called you in, Robert. It's transplant time."

Now Rob understood. He sprang out of bed.

"742," he said.

His father shook his head and smiled once more. "Look at your watch," he said.

Rob did. It was way after midnight. "743 days I've been waiting." He grabbed the bag which had sat by his bed, packed and ready, for the last two years.

"No more kidney machines," he said. "No more tired-all-the-time. No more can't-do-holidays. No more can't-eat-that, mustn't-drink-this. Energy! Freedom!!"

"Steady on, Rob. There are a few hurdles to cross first," said his father.

His mother stepped into the room with a towel and some clothes. "Like getting dressed," she said, as she laid them on the bed. His favourite Real Madrid shirt was on top. He put it on as if he was about to step out to play in a final – and then he remembered that even Real Madrid lost sometimes.

Out in the hall-way Rob saw his sister Kate, holding onto the banister with one hand and her teddy bear with the other. When she caught his eye she waved the teddy bear's paw at him.

"Go and get your kidney," she said, with a yawn. She waved again, this time with her own hand. "Kidney Kid."

"Ready?" asked Mum, when he had finished dressing. Rob looked at her, at his

15

father, at Kate. He picked up his bag. "Ready,"
he said.

He didn't feel it.

The next two hours felt as much like a
dream as an alien space fight. Mrs Carter
came in from next door to look after Kate,
while Rob and his parents all climbed into
the car. They drove west on the empty night-
time motorway towards the hospital.

At the hospital entrance a nurse met them and took them straight to the ward, where everyone seemed to be waiting for him. He was shown to a bed, where a nurse put a plastic label on his wrist. She gave him a funny-looking blue gown and asked him to change into it.

"Real Madrid, eh?" she asked, as he took his top off.

He nodded.

"So let me guess. You want to be a footballer."

He shook his head. "No. A pilot. A helicopter pilot."

"Good for you," she said. "Pilots get all kinds of medical tests, don't they? So you won't mind if we do a few now?"

She didn't wait for his answer before strapping a blood pressure cuff to his right arm. A doctor came in and asked a lot of questions. She shone a light in his eyes, looked in his mouth, listened to his chest, poked him in the belly, and hit his knees with a rubber hammer. "You'll do," she said, with a tired smile, as she stuck a needle in his arm to get a blood sample.

· Soon afterwards Rob was being pushed on a trolley down a long, bright lit corridor. The lights over-head flashed past like thought missiles. A nurse walked in front holding his medical records and X-rays, while a hospital porter pushed the trolley. His mum and dad walked along beside him, holding each other's hand. They stopped at a big double door.

The nurse turned to his parents. "Think of this as the school gates," she said. "And you're just dropping him off."

Rob looked at the nurse, and then at his parents. "What if I don't like school?" he asked.

Everybody laughed, the doors opened, and they wheeled Rob in.

It was a small room with shiny tiles, very bright lights, and no windows. Another doctor said hello. She reached for his arm, checked his name label, and put a tiny plastic tube into a vein on the back of his hand before he even noticed.

"Think of the last nice dream you had," she said, as she started to inject a clear liquid into the tube in his hand. "You'll soon feel very sleepy."

Rob looked up as she slipped her face mask on. She was ringed by bright lights and strange beeping machines, and when she spoke again her voice was different. Like a Dalek. Like an alien. "As you fall asleep, tell me your name and where you are in your dream."

"I'm Captain Robert Murray. Space Patrol. Fighter XQ 359."

Captain Murray looked at the alien commander as it bent over him. One of its long thin tentacles slithered over his hand. He pulled his arm away. "Truth drug or not," he said. "I'm telling you nothing else."

Organs and Transplants

1. Inside our bodies, as well as kidneys, we have other organs. In the chest you'll find the heart and two lungs. And in the belly are crammed two kidneys, one liver, a pancreas (say: pan-cree-as), the stomach, the guts, the bladder and more.

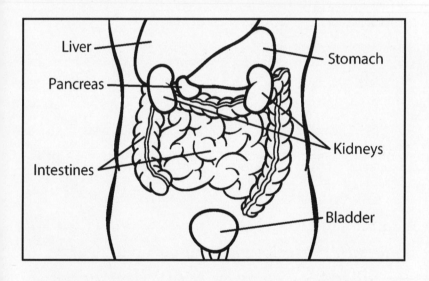

2. Accidents and illness can affect these organs, in lots of different ways. Doctors can often fix them with drugs and operations – but not always.

3. Some organs can be transplanted from one person to another. This involves two tricky operations – one to take the organ out, and one to put it in. These sometimes happen in different hospitals far apart.

4. If the organs are cooled down and carefully looked after, they can last for a while between being taken out and being put in. It's best if this time is as short as possible, and not more than a few hours.

5. This means doctors and nurses sometimes rush organs in helicopters (or even on motor-bikes) between hospitals.

Chapter 3
"I'm Making Pee!"

Rob opened his eyes. He stared at the
curtain rail over his bed, while he worked out
where he was and what had happened.

He remembered a race to hospital in the
middle of the night. He remembered a Dalek
doctor putting long tentacles on his arm.
After that he couldn't be certain what was
memory and what was a dream. He was sure
he had been a space pilot in an alien prison,
where aliens dressed in blue and green came

and went, talking a language he did not
understand and sticking sharp claws into
him. They had let his mum and dad visit, but
not Kate. This must have been because she
would help him escape.

He looked about for aliens or visitors.
There weren't any, though he recognised
Dad's bag on the floor. He was in a little
room, big enough for his bed and some empty
chairs. A locker stood by his bed, covered
with cards saying 'Get Well Soon'. A Real
Madrid shirt hung on the wall – with his own
name on the back!

A stand near the head of the bed held a
clear plastic bag, with a tube that ran down
to his left arm, where it slipped under a
bandage. Stuff like water dripped slowly
down it. He twisted to look further, and felt a
tightness, and a pain, in his side, low down,
on the right. It was the pain that told him
what had happened, because he knew this

was where the doctors put new kidneys when they did a transplant.

His right arm wasn't attached to any tubes. He slid his hand down, under the stiff white sheet, to feel his side, where the pain was. There was a bandage, and underneath it a swelling. He touched it gently. Could it be true? Could there be a new kidney under there?

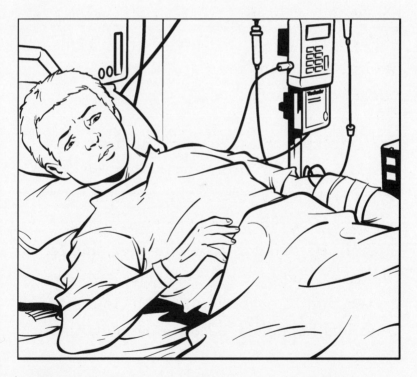

The door opened and in came the nurse who had taken him for his transplant. She looked nothing like an alien, but she seemed to think he was a space pilot.

"Good morning, Captain Murray," she said. "I'm Nancy."

"Hello, Nancy," Rob said. He couldn't think of anything else to say. She seemed very cheerful, so he thought she must have good news for him.

"Have I ... Have I –"

"Have you had a transplant? Yes."

"Is it working?"

She held up a bag which was clipped to his bed, with a tube that ran up under the sheets. It was full of pee. She smiled. "Oh, yes. It's working very well."

Rob couldn't believe it. Having a pee was so normal that other people never really thought about it. When he told them he hadn't had a pee for nearly two years, they thought he was joking. And now here was his new kidney, working away, making pee.

He looked around the room again, to be sure there wasn't a kidney machine there, hiding in the corner, then back at Nancy.

"Everything's going fine," she said. "We'll have you out of bed tomorrow, and up and about soon after that."

Dad came into the room, with a mobile phone in his hand. He looked tired.

"Hey there, son," he said. "Awake at last?"

"Hi, Dad."

"Sorry I wasn't here when you woke up. I was on the phone to Mum. Telling her the good news –"

"About the transplant?"

Dad put the phone away in his bag. "That's not news, son. Happened two days ago. You've been out of it for a while. No, I just went out to tell Mum that your kidney is working, doing what kidneys do. And now there's more good news to tell her."

"What's that?"

"You're awake and making sense again. No more talk about space pilots and aliens."

Rob didn't say anything.

Dad smiled. "Mum and I have taken it in turns to stay with you. You've been going on and on about thought missiles and truth drugs."

Rob blushed, while his dad patted his head. "Don't worry, you're not cracking up. It's the drugs the doctors used to knock you out. They are pretty strong."

"Will you tell Mum I'm back on Earth now?"

"You can tell her yourself. She's coming in tonight, with Kate."

Dialysis

1. All kinds of illness can cause kidney failure. Doctors and nurses can help treat most of them, but once kidney failure has gone a long way (doctors call it **end stage**) it can't be fixed.

2. That doesn't mean they can't help any more. They can attach you to kidney machines which do the job of your own kidneys. The treatment has a funny name – **dialysis** (say it: die-al-is-is).

3. There are two kinds of dialysis. One involves putting a tube through your belly and sloshing special liquid in and out three or four times a day. You can do this at home. For the other – the kind Rob has – you have to go to hospital three times a week for half a day. Nurses put needles in a vein in your arm, and attach you to a

machine. It takes out some of your blood, cleans and filters it, and puts it back.

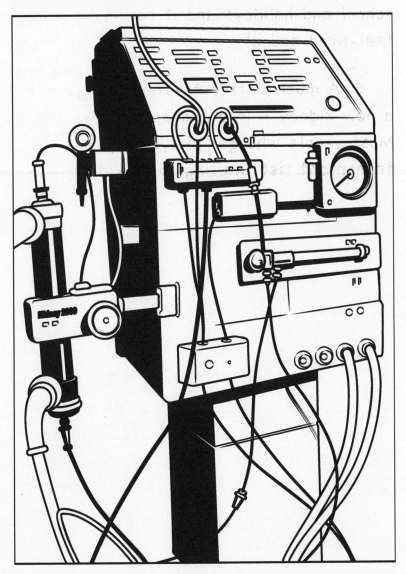

4. You can manage for a long time on dialysis, but it can get in the way of school and holidays and it can make you feel tired and ill.

5. A much better treatment is to get a new kidney – in a **transplant**, like Rob. Most people who get dialysis are on a **transplant list**, waiting for a kidney.

Chapter 4
Captain Murray – Space Pilot

Kate was excited when she arrived with Mum that evening. Dad tried to calm her down before he went home for a rest, but it didn't work.

"Can I see it?" Kate asked.

"See what?" said Rob.

"Your new kidney. Please?"

"There's nothing much to see. Just a cut where the doctors put it in."

"Well, can I see that?"

Rob wasn't sure. He looked at his Mum. The nurses had taken the bandage off that afternoon, and he hadn't really dared look at it himself since then.

"It will be all right to look at it, Kate," said Mum. "Just don't touch."

Rob pulled the sheet to one side, and pulled up his T-shirt. Low down on his belly, on the right side, a neat cut ran cross-ways. Some metal clips held the edges together, and between them the skin was a bit bruised.

Mum pointed out the way the cut swelled outwards. "Rob's new kidney's just underneath, Kate. So when he gets well, and comes home, we all have to be careful not to bump him there."

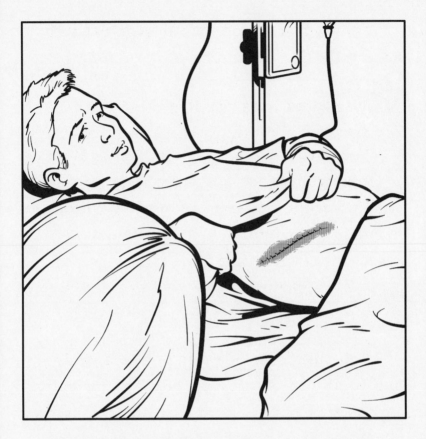

Kate came up close to get a good look. "Does it hurt?" Kate asked.

"A bit, but only when I move, or cough, or laugh."

"So don't say anything funny, Kate," said Mum, as she sat back down.

Kate stared at the cut, then looked from Mum to Rob. "Where did it come from?"

Rob looked to his mother. He had wondered too, but didn't like to ask.

Mum put on her serious face. "It's Robbie's kidney now, Kate. But you're right, it did come from someone else. Someone very kind, with a very kind family. That person carried a donor card. It said if something bad happened to them, and they died from an illness or an accident, they wanted their organs to go to other people like Rob, to help them."

"So what was it?" asked Kate.

"Hmm?"

"An illness or an accident?"

"We don't know, Kate. The doctors and nurses are not allowed to tell us much."

"What does this person's family know about me?" asked Rob. He couldn't help thinking about the car crash on the motorway.

"Nothing," said Mum. "Not yet, anyway." Now she smiled the way she did when she wanted him to do his homework. "But when you feel ready you can write a letter to them. If we give it to the nurses they will make sure the donor's family gets it."

Kate bounced up and down in her chair. "What will you tell them about me?" she asked.

Rob looked seriously at her. "I'll say you are the most nosey, most noisy, most annoying little sister in the world."

Kate frowned, but Rob just smiled back. "But I'm glad that now I don't need the kidney machine any more, we can all go away on holiday together. Where would you like to go?"

"Italy. Finland. Japan. Everywhere." She started giggling, and looked at Mum. "The moon. Maybe Mars."

Rob blushed and he too looked at Mum. "Please say you didn't tell her about –"

"Captain Murray, space pilot?" giggled Kate. "I know all about him."

Rob pulled the sheet over his head and groaned. He would never hear the end of this.

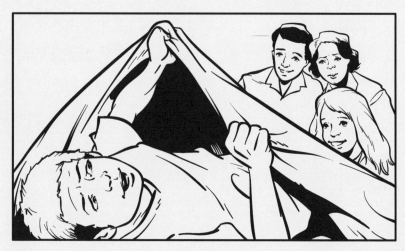

Rob lay back on his bed and stared up at the ceiling. The room was dark and silent. Dad was due in later, so Rob was on his own. The nurses thought he was asleep, but there was too much to think about, and anyway he didn't feel right. He was hot, and the sheets felt sweaty under his back.

He knew his mum had said not to touch, but he couldn't help running his hand down to the cut in his side. He touched the skin above the cut and felt the outline of the kidney underneath. He wondered about the donor, the person whose kidney it had been. He remembered the car crash on the motorway, and he remembered wishing the driver would make it, as the air ambulance flew away.

But if that was the person, he thought, *and they had made it, then I wouldn't have this transplant. This kidney would still be where it started off, inside that person,*

instead of here, inside me. And I'd still have
to hook up to the kidney machine three times
a week.

He didn't want to think about that. His
new kidney would be older than he was. He
thought about where it had been, in those
extra years. He hoped he would now be able
to go to new places, and to do new things. He
started to make lists, beginning with Kate's
choices (*Italy ... Finland ... Japan*).

Thoughts like this went round and round
in his head, until he started to feel sick. It
was then he heard a helicopter's engine. He
sat up quickly, feeling a sharp tug where his
kidney was, but the bed was too far from the
window to see.

He wasn't meant to get out of bed – but a
helicopter was coming in to land, right
outside his room, and he just had to see it.
He swung his legs to the floor, stood up

shakily, and shuffled across to the window, being careful to take with him all the tubes he was still attached to.

On the ground below, not far away, was a large flat area, with a big white circle painted on it. Inside the circle was a huge letter H. People stood close by, waiting and looking up at the lights of a helicopter as it came in to land. The moment it touched down, a door opened in its side, and two people dressed in white stepped out. Rob expected them to have a stretcher with them, bringing someone in for emergency treatment. But all they carried was a white box, marked with a red cross. They handed it over to some of the waiting people, and everyone hurried towards the hospital entrance together.

Rob felt dizzy with the effort of getting up. New thoughts ran through his mind. *Was that a kidney? A heart? A liver? Where had it*

come from? Who would be getting the call
tonight, the call for a transplant, the call
that would change their life?

The lights on the heli-pad grew blurred
and dim. The engine noise faded away. The
bed seemed to move from side to side. He

reached for the wall to steady himself. The button to call the nurse was back on the bed. He wasn't sure he could get there without collapsing, but he had to try. He turned and stepped forward, then lost all strength in his legs. *Don't bump the kidney!* he thought, as he fell to the floor.

The lights snapped on and the door swung open. "*Rob!*" shouted Dad, as he dashed forward. He called for the nurses and bent down – just in time for Rob to be sick all over his new shoes.

Donors

1. Kidneys and other organs have to be **matched** with the people who need them. Matching depends on your blood group and other things to do with your DNA.

2. When an organ becomes available, transplant teams go through their lists to find who it would match best with. This has to be done very quickly, often in the middle of the night. When they find the right person they ring them up and ask them to come to hospital straight away.

3. Organs normally come from people who have just died in an accident or from an illness.

4. These people have said before they fall ill that they want to be an **organ donor**. They carry a little card to say what they want to happen when they die,

and their names are on a computer list called the **donor register**.

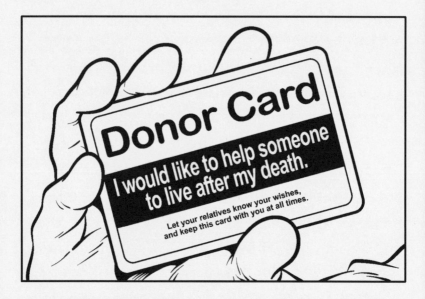

5. A donor can give one heart, two lungs, two kidneys, a liver (which can be split in two) and a pancreas. So they can help eight different people who are waiting for transplants.

6. Families of people who die feel very sad but it can help them to know that the person they have lost has helped others by donating organs.

7. Sadly there are not enough organs to go round. People are waiting longer and longer before they get called in for a transplant.

8. So more transplants are being done where the organ comes from a living person. This happens most in the case of kidneys. A healthy person can normally give up one of their kidneys and manage fine on the one they have left.

9. **Living donors** are normally members of the family. Their organs also have to match. Rob's mum and dad both wanted to give him one of their kidneys, but blood tests showed they didn't match, so it wouldn't work.

Chapter 5
Iceberg!

"It might be rejection that's making you ill," said the doctor. She stood beside Rob, who was safely back in his bed, cleaned up but still feeling rough. Dad sat on the other side, wiping his shoes.

"That's when your body, your immune system, tries to fight off the new kidney," the doctor said.

"Can you do anything about it?" Rob asked. He was worried – the new kidney had only been in for a few days and already there were problems.

"Yes," said the doctor. "There are lots of pills and injections we can use to control it." She smiled, to try and reduce his worries. Rob didn't smile back. There had to be a catch.

"But …"

Rob sighed. "I knew there'd be a but. There always is."

"It's not a big but," the doctor said. "To treat rejection we have to be sure that's what is going on in the new kidney."

"How do you do that?"

"We take a tiny piece of it away. It's called a biopsy."

"A what?" asked Rob.

"A bi-op-see," said the doctor.

"And how do you *that?*"

"We use a needle."

Rob groaned. He'd had so many needles stuck in him over the years. "What, you just stick it in?"

The doctor smiled again. "There's a bit more to it than that … but basically yes."

He turned to Dad. "Is this what I get for chucking up on your shoes, Dad?"

Dad laughed, put his shoe down, and laid his hand on his son's arm. "You're not being punished for anything, Rob. And the shoes have cleaned up fine."

Rob looked up at the doctor. "So when does this happen?"

"Now."

"Right here?"

The doctor nodded. "I want you to lie back, as still as you can. See the posters up on the ceiling?" There were pictures of space, as well as the jungle, the desert and the arctic. Rob had wondered what they were there for. Now he knew. "Choose one and focus on it. Make up a story that happens there."

Rob lay back while the doctor prepared her equipment. The door opened to let Nancy in. "I know which poster you've chosen, Mr Space-man," she said.

Rob grinned up at her. "Bet you don't," he said.

Rob felt a poking and prodding at his belly. He looked down briefly, to see a long hollow needle glinting in the light.

"Best not to look, son," said Dad. "I'll do the looking for you. You keep your mind on that poster. What are you now – Jungle Jim, or a desert rat?"

"All right, Robbie," said Nancy. "You need to lie *very* still now. You'll feel a push ..."

He did. *I'm an iceberg*, he thought. *Totally still. Can't feel a thing.*

"– and now a sharp jab –"

Again, he did. *Iceberg!*

"Good lad," said Dad.

"And that's it. Done, finished," said Nancy, brightly. She was pressing on the spot where the doctor had taken the needle out. "You were very brave."

"I was just thinking of the person whose kidney it was," said Rob. "I want to look after it properly."

After A Transplant

1. We have an **immune system** which normally fights off illness and infection. After a transplant this system will try to fight off the new organ. It's called **rejection**.

2. Doctors use tablets and injections to stop rejection happening. After a transplant you have to take these tablets for the rest of your life. You also need regular blood tests, and sometimes X-rays and scans, and even a biopsy, like Rob had.

3. It sounds like a lot – but it is much better than being on a kidney machine.

4. Transplants can last a long time if they are looked after properly – but they don't last for ever. Some people end up with more than one!

Chapter 6
Flight School

Three weeks later Rob was packing the last of his '*Get Well*' cards away. He was no longer attached to any tubes, and instead of hospital pyjamas he proudly wore his Real Madrid shirt, with the number 1 and the name 'Rob' on the back. He looked and felt well – and he still enjoyed the fact he could pee again, just like any other boy.

The biopsy had told the doctors what was wrong. They changed his tablets around, and he felt better so quickly they said he could go home. He wasn't sick again. The cut on his side was healing well, and the clips on his skin had been taken off.

He looked out of the window to the big white H in its circle. He'd enjoyed watching the helicopters take off and land but now he couldn't wait to go home.

Kate barged into the room, with Mum and Dad following. They were carrying boxes of chocolates and other presents to give to the nurses for looking after Rob so well.

"Come on, then, Kidney Kid," said Kate.

Nancy came into the room to say good-bye. Dad gave her the chocolates and a kiss. She got embarrassed and Mum looked at Dad with a frown.

Nancy turned to Rob. "What have you got planned for when you get home, young man?"

"Before anything else I've got a letter to write," said Rob. "An important letter."

"Take your time over it," said Nancy. "Make a start, maybe. There's no hurry to finish."

"And then ... School!" said Mum. "Have you missed it?"

Rob shook his head. "No. But when I go back they won't be able to call me Kidney Kid any more. I'll just be normal."

"No excuses now about homework and exams, though, Rob," said Dad.

"That's OK," said Rob. "I won't need any."

"Oh?" asked Mum.

"Yes," said Nancy. "He'll have to pass all his exams now."

Dad chuckled and turned to Mum. "Sounds like he's had a brain transplant too," he said.

Nancy smiled at Rob. "Why don't you tell them?" she urged.

Rob looked from Mum to Dad. Even Kate was eager to hear what he had to say. "Before the transplant, I could only be a pilot in my dreams –"

Kate giggled. "You mean like Captain Murray?"

"Shh, Katie," said Mum. "Let him speak."

Rob smiled at his sister. "I want to be a real pilot, here on Earth. Before, I never thought I could. Now, with my new kidney, I have a chance. And I'm going to take it."

"Wow," said Dad.

"Hmm," said Mum. She wasn't sure yet.

"So, yes," Rob went on. "There will be loads of exams and practice and tests. But that's OK. I even know what kind of pilot I want to be."

He turned towards the window, and looked down at the white H again. He knew it stood for Helicopter, but to him now it would always mean Hope.

"I'm going to fly a helicopter. A *hospital* helicopter."

"Good, for you," said Nancy, as she held open the door for him. "I hope you make it. I really do."

Living with a Transplant

1. People who get transplants don't feel tired all the time, like they do on dialysis. They can do more, both at work and at home with their families. They can travel, and go on holidays, because they don't need to attach to kidney machines.

2. They can even play sport! The famous New Zealand rugby player, Jonah Lomu, returned to top level rugby after he had a kidney transplant.

3. Lots of countries have their own Transplant Games, and every two years there is the World Transplant Games – a kind of Olympics for people who have had transplants. There's even a **Winter** Transplant Games, where people race down mountains on skis and snow-boards!

AUTHOR FACT FILE
STEPHEN POTTS

We all know about transplants, new kidneys, new livers, new hearts etc. What gave you the idea to write a book about them?

I work with the transplant unit in my hospital, so I have seen how much a transplant can change someone's life for the better.

Have you ever had to have an operation?

Yes. I rowed a lot at university. I was out in a boat when I got a piece of an oar stuck in my hand. I needed plastic surgery, and I missed a month of training.

Have you ever flown in a helicopter?

Yes, but only once, on a trip to Greenland. I was sailing and climbing in the mountains and fjords there. Our boat was stuck in the ice and the only way to get back to it was by helicopter. What I remember most is the noise.

When you were younger, what did you most want to do in life?

Until I was five I wanted to drive a dustbin lorry. After that, all I ever wanted was to be a doctor.

ILLUSTRATOR FACT FILE
NIGEL DOBBYN

Have you ever had to have an operation in hospital?

No, thank God.

Have you ever been in an emergency?

I had my foot run over by a double decker bus when I was twelve. It was amazing that it didn't break any bones. The doctor said they must be made of rubber!

Have you ever flown in a helicopter?

I did an abseil down from a navy helicopter onto a harbour wall when I was at school.

When you were younger, what did you most want to do in life?

To draw comic strips or to go to the moon. I have done one of them.

What's your favourite medical film or TV show?

ER.

Barrington Stoke would like to thank all its readers for commenting on the manuscript before publication and in particular:

Become a Consultant!

Would you like to give us feedback on our titles before they are published? Contact us at the email address below – we'd love to hear from you!

info@barringtonstoke.co.uk
www.barringtonstoke.co.uk